# German
*GCSE ROLE PLAYS*
**for AQA**

*higher*
workbook

# German
## GCSE ROLE PLAYS
## for AQA

# higher
## workbook

## Sue Smart
## Series author: Jean-Claude Gilles

## JOHN MURRAY

*Also in this series:*
*French GCSE Role Plays for AQA* Foundation Workbook     ISBN 0 7195 8143 5
(pack of 10)
*French GCSE Role Plays for AQA* Higher Workbook     ISBN 0 7195 8146 X
(pack of 10)
*French GCSE Role Plays for AQA* Audio on CD     ISBN 0 7195 8151 6
*Spanish GCSE Role Plays for AQA* Foundation Workbook     ISBN 0 7195 8162 1
(pack of 10)
*Spanish GCSE Role Plays for AQA* Higher Workbook     ISBN 0 7195 8163 X
(pack of 10)
*Spanish GCSE Role Plays for AQA* Audio on CD     ISBN 0 7195 8160 5

© Sue Smart 2003

First published 2003
by John Murray Publishers Ltd, a member of the Hodder Headline Group
338 Euston Road, London NW1 3BH

Cover design by John Townson/Creation
Typeset in 10/13pt Times Ten Roman by Fakenham Photosetting Ltd, Fakenham,
Norfolk NR21 8NN
Printed and bound in Great Britain by St Edmundsbury Press, Bury St Edmunds

A CIP catalogue record for this book is available from the British Library.

Foundation Workbook     ISBN 0 7195 8164 8 (pack of 10)
Higher Workbook     ISBN 0 7195 8165 6 (pack of 10)
Audio on CD     ISBN 0 7195 8161 3

# CONTENTS

# INTRODUCTION

This booklet offers 30 different role plays for practice. All role plays have been used in the AQA GCSE speaking tests. The booklet can be used in different ways:

- You can work in pairs.
- One partner uses the candidate's script whilst the other provides the prompt from the teacher's script. Both partners can get involved in the marking of the performance.
- Extra help can be found in the vocabulary section on pages 61–2.
- For a more challenging role play, cover up the 'To help you' section.
- You could record your performance and compare it to the recording that accompanies the booklet.
- You could work independently and complete the task by:
  - looking at the candidate's role only
  - looking at both the candidate's and the teacher's roles
  - using the 'To help you' section
  - using the vocabulary section on pages 61–2.

Using the suggestions above allows for a gradual preparation for the exam task itself. Regular practice will help you familiarise yourself with the format and the demands of the task and remove some of the anxieties you may feel when faced with speaking German in an exam situation.

I also recommend that you listen to the recording regularly and work on improving your pronunciation. Although pronunciation is not included in the assessment criteria, it is taken into account in as much as it affects communication. Candidates do lose marks if it is thought that a sympathetic native speaker would not understand what has been said or if poor pronunciation results in ambiguity.

The role play is the first task of the GCSE speaking test. A confident performance will set you up for the rest of the test.

## ■ THE MARK SCHEMES

The mark schemes included in this booklet illustrate the Criteria for Assessment, as found in the AQA specification.

### Criteria for assessment
### Higher role play – Communication and quality of language

| | |
|---|---|
| 0 marks | Required message not communicated. |
| 1 mark | Appropriate response, although inaccuracy or loss of part of the message may cause difficulty or ambiguity for comprehension. The task may not be fully accomplished, but some relevant information is communicated. |
| 2 marks | Appropriate and unambiguous response, although there may be minor errors or omission of a minor element of the message. |
| 3 marks | Appropriate and full response. Quality of language is such that minor errors would cause no difficulties of comprehension. |

4 marks    Appropriate and correct response. The task is accomplished fully and without significant error, meaning that the response is grammatically correct but may contain one minor error. If an answer contains more than one minor error, 3 marks maximum may be awarded.

WARNING TO TEACHERS!
At Higher Tier, the teacher's script is not prescriptive and there is therefore more flexibility. However, because the candidate's role is unstructured, it is essential that you are clear about the tasks which the candidate must accomplish. You may change the target language phrases if necessary, e.g. if the candidate's response makes it inappropriate. However, you should remember that if you supply key vocabulary, candidates cannot be rewarded for it.

## ■ ABBREVIATIONS IN THE MARK SCHEME
**OCR**    otherwise correct response
**WO**    word order

I acknowledge with thanks AQA for giving me permission to publish the role plays in this booklet.

# CANDIDATE'S ROLE

> You have had an accident whilst on holiday in Germany. You go to the hospital.
>
> **a)** • *Unfall.*
> **b)** • *Symptome (zwei Details).*
> **c)** • *Wie. Wo.*
> **d)** •
>
> When you see  you will have to respond to something which you have not prepared.
>
> Your teacher will play the part of the doctor and will speak first.

## ■ TO HELP YOU

**a)** The English introduction should help you to decide what you need to say, particularly for the first answer. Watch the tense – which one do you need?

**b)** Make sure you do give two details, otherwise marks will be lost.

**c)** The prompts often contain question words – make sure you know all the main ones. Again, there will be two parts to the answer here.

**d)** Try to think what sort of information might be required here – it is likely to be something to do with contacting you/someone else.

## ■ JOT DOWN YOUR ANSWERS

**a)** _____

_____

**b)** _____

_____

**c)** _____

_____

**d)** _____

_____

# TEACHER'S ROLE

1   Begin the conversation by explaining the situation and asking the candidate what has happened.
    *Du bist ins Krankenhaus gegangen. Ich bin der Arzt/die Ärztin. Was ist passiert?*

2   Allow the candidate to say that he/she has had an accident.
    Ask what is wrong. Elicit two details.
    *Beschreiben Sie Ihre Symptome.*

3   Allow the candidate to give two details about his/her symptoms.
    Ask the candidate how it happened and where.
    *Wie ist der Unfall passiert? Wo?*

4   **!** Allow the candidate to say how and where it happened.
    Ask the candidate whom you should contact. Ask how the person can be contacted.
    *Wen soll ich informieren? Wie kann ich das machen?*

5   Allow the candidate to say whom you should contact and how the person can be contacted.
    End the conversation by saying thank you.
    *Danke.*

NB   You should address the candidate as *Sie* throughout this role play.

| OCR | otherwise correct response |
|-----|----------------------------|
| WO  | word order |

## ■ MARK SCHEME

|    | 0 | 1 | 2 | 3 | 4 |
|----|---|---|---|---|---|
| **a)** | *Unfall* on its own | *Ein Unfall ist passiert* | | | *Ich habe einen Unfall gehabt* |
| **b)** | | One element missing | | *Ich habe mein Arm verletzt und meine Kopf tut weh* (two minor errors) | Any two appropriate details |
| **c)** | | One element missing | Present tense for one element in **OCR** | | |
| **d)** | | One element missing | Present tense for one element in **OCR** | | *Meine Mutter. Die Telefonnummer ist . . .* |

# ROLE PLAY 2

## CANDIDATE'S ROLE

> You are telling your Austrian friend about your local area and a recent visit to a concert.
>
> **a)**   • *Konzert.*
> **b)**   • *Deine Meinung.*
> **c)**   • ❗
> **d)**   • *Andere Freizeitaktivitäten in der Gegend (drei Details).*
>
> When you see ❗ you will have to respond to something which you have not prepared.
>
> Your teacher will play the part of your friend and will speak first.

### ■ TO HELP YOU

**a)**  The English introduction makes it clear that you will have to use the past tense somewhere in your answer.

**b)**  Make sure you know a variety of positive and negative opinions and can say why you have that opinion – using *gut* is unlikely to gain you the top marks.

**c)**  Remember, this is where you really must listen very carefully to what the teacher says. Often there are two parts to this task, which are usually asked separately, so listen especially carefully to the question words and try to remember the tense of the question.

**d)**  Make sure during your preparation time that you have got three details as required.

### ■ JOT DOWN YOUR ANSWERS

**a)**  _____

_____

**b)**  _____

_____

**c)**  _____

_____

**d)**  _____

_____

# TEACHER'S ROLE

1   Begin the conversation by asking the candidate if he/she has recently been out.
*Du sprichst mit deinem österreichischen Freund/deiner österreichischen Freundin. Ich bin der Freund/die Freundin. Bist du neulich ausgegangen?*

2   Allow the candidate to say that he/she went to a concert.
Ask the candidate what sort of concert it was and what he/she thought of it.
*Was für ein Konzert war das? Wie hat es dir gefallen?*

3   ❗ Allow the candidate to say what sort of concert it was and what he/she thought of it.
Ask how the candidate travelled to the concert. Ask why he/she did not use . . . (alternative form of transport).
*Wie bist du zum Konzert gefahren? Warum bist du nicht (. . .) gefahren?*

4   Allow the candidate to say how he/she travelled to the concert and why.
Ask the candidate what else there is to do in the area. Elicit three details, other than concerts.
*Was gibt es sonst noch hier in der Gegend zu tun?*

5   Allow the candidate to give three details about what else there is to do in the area.
End the conversation by saying that's interesting.
*Das ist aber interessant.*

| OCR | otherwise correct response |
|-----|----------------------------|
| WO  | word order                 |

NB   You should address the candidate as *du* throughout this role play.

## ■ MARK SCHEME

|     | 0 | 1 | 2 | 3 | 4 |
|-----|---|---|---|---|---|
| **a)** | Wrong tense | *habe . . . + infinitive* | *Ich bin ein Konzert besucht* | | *Ich bin zu einem Konzert gegangen* |
| **b)** | | One element missing *Es war gut* | | | *Das war ein Rockkonzert und es war prima* |
| **c)** | *bei/auf Bus* for the 'how' part of the utterance | One element missing | | *Ich bin mit das Auto gefahren, denn die Bus ist zu langsam* (two minor errors) | |
| **d)** | | One element only given | Two elements only given | | *Man kann den Dom besuchen, es gibt ein Museum, und man kann ins Kino gehen* At least two activities + one detail OR three activities |

# CANDIDATE'S ROLE

> Your German friend is thinking of going on a language course in the USA next summer. You are certain that your friend would be better off coming to Britain to learn English.
>
> **a)** • *Deine Meinung.*
> **b)** • *Zwei Gründe warum.*
> **c)** • *Wo in Großbritannien. Warum.*
> **d)** • !
>
> When you see ! you will have to respond to something which you have not prepared.
>
> Your teacher will play the part of your friend and will speak first.

## ■ TO HELP YOU

**a)** The English introduction should help you to decide what you need to say, particularly for the first answer. Make sure the opinion you give fits the situation.

**b)** Make sure you do give two reasons, otherwise marks will be lost. Use your preparation time carefully to think of suitable reasons.

**c)** Again there will be two parts to the answer here.

**d)** Try to think what sort of information might be required here – whether you manage that or not, it is vital that you listen really carefully to what the teacher says when you get to the ! task.

## ■ JOT DOWN YOUR ANSWERS

**a)** _____

_____

**b)** _____

_____

**c)** _____

_____

**d)** _____

_____

# TEACHER'S ROLE

1 Begin the conversation by saying you want to do a language course in the USA.
*Du telefonierst mit deinem deutschen Freund/deiner deutschen Freundin. Ich bin der Freund/die Freundin. Ich möchte einen Sprachkurs in den USA machen. Was meinst du?*

2 Allow the candidate to say he/she thinks a course in Britain would be better.
Ask why a course in Britain would be better. Elicit two reasons.
*Warum wäre ein Kurs in Großbritannien besser?*

3 Allow the candidate to give two reasons why a course in Britain would be better.
Ask the candidate which part of Britain he/she would recommend and why.
*Welche Gegend in Großbritannien würdest du empfehlen? Warum?*

4 ⚠ Allow the candidate to recommend a part of Britain and say why.
Ask the candidate how you can get more information about that part of the country.
*Wie kann ich weitere Informationen bekommen?*

5 Allow the candidate to explain how to get information about that part of the country.
End the conversation by saying you will go to Britain instead of the USA.
*Gut. Ich werde also nach Großbritannien fahren.*

| OCR | otherwise correct response |
|-----|---------------------------|
| WO | word order |

NB    You should address the candidate as *du* throughout this role play.

## ■ MARK SCHEME

|  | 0 | 1 | 2 | 3 | 4 |
|---|---|---|---|---|---|
| a) | *Das ist eine gute Idee* | | | | *Das ist keine gute Idee/Ich glaube, ein Sprachkurs in Großbritannien wäre besser* |
| b) | | One element missing | *Es ist gut und interessant* | Two minor errors in **OCR** | *Es gibt viele Kurse hier, und die Leute sind freundlich* |
| c) | | No reason given in **OCR** | Reason only given in **OCR** | | *Du kannst mich besuchen und neue Leute kennen lernen* |
| d) | | | | | Any appropriate response |

# CANDIDATE'S ROLE

> You are staying with a German family and return home very late one night after a party. Your host is very concerned.
>
> a)     • *Deine Entschuldigung.*
> b)     • *Warum kein Telefonanruf.*
> c)     •
> d)     • *Pläne für heute Abend (zwei Details).*
>
> When you see ! you will have to respond to something which you have not prepared.
>
> Your teacher will play the part of your German host and will speak first.

## ■ TO HELP YOU

a) Try to use the prompt to think of the obvious way to apologise – you would normally say sorry and explain where you have been. Think which tense you need here.

b) Your answer does not have to be lengthy, just correct – the response here can be very simple. What is an obvious reason for not having phoned?

c) Listen carefully, and also try to think beforehand what a concerned host might ask at this point.

d) This is a standard task at Higher Tier and is not difficult, providing you remember to give all the details required and with two verbs. Minimal responses such as *Tennis und Schwimmen* do not communicate fully and will be marked accordingly.

## ■ JOT DOWN YOUR ANSWERS

a) _____

_____

b) _____

_____

c) _____

_____

d) _____

_____

# TEACHER'S ROLE

1 Begin the conversation by saying that you were really worried that the candidate came home so late. Ask what he/she has to say and where he/she was.
*Du wohnst bei deinem deutschen Freund/deiner deutschen Freundin. Ich bin sein Vater/seine Mutter. Ich war wirklich besorgt, dass du so spät nach Hause zurückgekommen bist. Wo warst du?*

2 Allow the candidate to apologise for the late return and to say where he/she was.
Ask the candidate why he/she did not telephone you.
*Warum hast du nicht angerufen?*

3 ❗ Allow the candidate to explain why he/she did not telephone you.
Say you do not find that acceptable. Ask what his/her parents would say about it.
*Das finde ich nicht gut. Was würden deine Eltern dazusagen?*

4 Allow the candidate to say what his/her parents would say.
Ask what he/she plans to do this evening. Elicit two details.
*Was hast du heute Abend vor?*

5 Allow the candidate to give two details of his/her plans for the evening.
End the conversation by saying that is OK.
*O.K. Das ist gut.*

NB   You should address the candidate as *du* throughout this role play.

| OCR | otherwise correct response |
|-----|-----|
| WO | word order |

## ■ MARK SCHEME

| | 0 | 1 | 2 | 3 | 4 |
|---|---|---|---|---|---|
| a) | | No apology in **OCR** | | Use of *bin spät* in **OCR** | *Es tut mir Leid, dass ich so spät zurückgekommen bin. Ich war in der Disko* |
| b) | | | | Two minor errors in **OCR** | *Ich hatte mein Handy nicht mit/Ich hatte kein Geld* |
| c) | | | | | *Meine Eltern sagen nichts/Das geht* |
| d) | | One detail only in **OCR** Use of continuous present in **OCR** | *Kino mit Freunden* | | *Ich treffe meine Freunde, und wir gehen ins Kino* |

**8**

# CANDIDATE'S ROLE

> You are at Frankfurt airport. You want to change your ticket to return to London urgently due to an illness in your family. You need to know if you have to pay more.
>
> **a)**    • *Ticket.*
> **b)**    • *Grund warum.*
> **c)**    • ❗
> **d)**    • *Preis.*
>
> When you see ❗ you will have to respond to something which you have not prepared.
>
> Your teacher will play the part of the travel agent and will speak first.

## ■ TO HELP YOU

**a)** If you cannot think of the verb you need, try and work out how to do the task in another way. You could say you need another/different ticket – certainly say something, rather than not saying anything because there is one word you don't know.

**b)** The overall scene setting tells you what to prepare here. Always look at it carefully!

**c)** Listen carefully and think what the travel agent is likely to be asking here.

**d)** This is a straightforward task, providing you remember to give all the detail required. Just asking the price is not enough, as it clearly mentions paying more in the instructions at the top.

## ■ JOT DOWN YOUR ANSWERS

**a)** _____

_____

**b)** _____

_____

**c)** _____

_____

**d)** _____

_____

## TEACHER'S ROLE

1   Introduce the conversation, then ask how you can help.
    *Wir sind am Frankfurter Flughafen. Ich bin der/die Angestellte. Wie kann ich Ihnen helfen?*

2   Allow the candidate to say he/she wants to change the ticket. Ask why.
    *Warum wollen Sie das machen?*

3   ❗ Allow the candidate to say why he/she has to return to London. Ask exactly when he/she wants to leave. Elicit the day and time.
    *Es tut mir Leid. Wann wollen Sie fliegen? Um wie viel Uhr?*

4   Allow the candidate to say exactly when he/she wants to leave. Say that is not a problem. Ask if that is all.
    *Kein Problem. Sonst noch etwas?*

5   Allow the candidate to ask about further payment. End the conversation by saying it is the same price.
    *Das ist derselbe Preis.*

| OCR | otherwise correct response |
|-----|---------------------------|
| WO  | word order                |

NB   You should address the candidate as *Sie* throughout this role play.

## ■ MARK SCHEME

|    | 0 | 1 | 2 | 3 | 4 |
|----|---|---|---|---|---|
| a) | Use of *umsteigen/ umziehen* Use of *Kleingeld* | Use of *möchte* in **OCR** | Incorrect **WO** with modal in **OCR** | | *Ich möchte meine Fahrkarte umtauschen* |
| b) | | | | Two minor errors in **OCR** | *Meine Mutter ist krank* |
| c) | | One detail missing in **OCR** | | | Appropriate response |
| d) | | | *Was kostet das?* | *Ist das mehr Geld?* | *Kostet das mehr? Muss ich mehr bezahlen?* |

10

# ROLE PLAY 6

## CANDIDATE'S ROLE

You are going on an exchange visit to Germany. You telephone your partner to make arrangements for meeting each other.

**a)** • *Dein Name. Anruf – warum.*
**b)** • *Ankunft – wann und wo.*
**c)** • **!**
**d)** • *Zwei Aktivitäten.*

When you see **!** you will have to respond to something which you have not prepared.

Your teacher will play the part of your partner and will speak first.

### ■ TO HELP YOU

**a)** This is very straightforward. Make sure you also have your reason ready.
**b)** Make sure you choose a time and a place you can pronounce correctly.
**c)** Listen carefully – what is the obvious thing an exchange partner might ask here?
**d)** This is a straightforward task and is not difficult, providing you remember to give all the details required and include two verbs. Minimal responses such as *Tennis und Schwimmen* do not communicate fully and will not gain you the maximum mark.

### ■ JOT DOWN YOUR ANSWERS

**a)** _____

_____

**b)** _____

_____

**c)** _____

_____

**d)** _____

_____

# TEACHER'S ROLE

1  Introduce the conversation, then give a name and ask who is calling.
   *Du telefonierst mit deinem deutschen Freund/deiner deutschen Freundin. Ich bin der Freund/die Freundin. Hallo, Wernicke. Wer spricht bitte?*

2  Allow the candidate to give his/her name and to say why he/she is telephoning.
   Ask when and where he/she will arrive.
   *Wann kommst du an, und wo?*

3  ▯ Allow the candidate to give time and place of arrival.
   Ask the candidate to describe him/herself. Elicit three details.
   *Kannst du dich beschreiben?*

4  Allow the candidate to describe him/herself, giving three details.
   Ask what he/she would like to do in Germany. Elicit two activities.
   *Was möchtest du hier in Deutschland machen?*

5  Allow the candidate to give two activities.
   End the conversation by saying you are looking forward to his/her visit.
   *Ich freue mich auf deinen Besuch.*

NB  You should address the candidate as *du* throughout this role play.

| OCR | otherwise correct response |
|-----|----------------------------|
| WO  | word order                 |

## ■ MARK SCHEME

|     | 0 | 1 | 2 | 3 | 4 |
|-----|---|---|---|---|---|
| a)  |   | Name only in **OCR** |   | Omission of name in **OCR** |   |
| b)  |   | Omission of one detail Use of continuous present in **OCR** |   |   | *Ich komme um 15 Uhr am Bahnhof an* |
| c)  |   | One detail only given | Two details only given | Full details with minor errors | Appropriate response, containing three details |
| d)  |   | One activity only in **OCR** | *Tennis und Schwimmen* Use of *m̲öchte* in **OCR** |   | *Ich möchte Tennis spielen und ein Museum besuchen* |

# ROLE PLAY
# 7
# CANDIDATE'S ROLE

> You are talking to your German friend about your last holiday. You also discuss your friend's holiday.
>
> a)  • *Deine letzten Ferien (zwei Details).*
> b)  • *Und dein Freund/deine Freundin?*
> c)  • *Dein Lieblingsferienland und warum.*
> d)  • ▉
>
> When you see ▉ you will have to respond to something which you have not prepared.
>
> Your teacher will play the part of your friend and will speak first.

## ■ TO HELP YOU

a) It is clear from the overall rubric and the *letzten* in the prompt that you will need to use the past tense here. Be careful with your auxiliary verb – will it be *Ich habe . . .* or *Ich bin . . .*?

b) The ? at the end tells you that you have to ask a question – a general question will be fine here.

c) This can easily be prepared in advance, but make sure you choose both a country you can pronounce and a reason that fits.

d) It is easier in some role plays than others to work out what this might be. If you are unsure, listen even more carefully than usual to what the teacher is asking. You can always ask for the question to be repeated – as long as the teacher does not give away key vocabulary this is perfectly acceptable.

## ■ JOT DOWN YOUR ANSWERS

a) _____

_____

b) _____

_____

c) _____

_____

d) _____

_____

**13**

# TEACHER'S ROLE

**1** Begin the conversation by asking the candidate to tell you about his/her holidays. Elicit two details.
*Erzähl mir von deinen letzten Ferien.*

**2** Allow the candidate to describe his/her last holiday, giving two details.
Say you were on holiday too.
*Ich war auch auf Urlaub.*

**3** Allow the candidate to ask what you did on your holiday.
Say you went to Italy to visit the museums and cathedrals. Ask which is his/her favourite holiday country and why.
*Ich bin nach Italien gefahren und habe viele Museen und Dome besichtigt. Was ist dein Lieblingsferienland? Warum?*

**4** ⚠ Allow the candidate to say which is his/her favourite holiday country and why.
Ask how he/she gets the money for holidays.
*Wie bekommst du Geld für deine Ferien?*

**5** Allow the candidate to say how he/she gets the money for holidays.
End the conversation by saying you would like to visit the candidate's favourite country too.
*Ich möchte auch . . . besuchen.*

| OCR | otherwise correct response |
|-----|----------------------------|
| WO | word order |

NB   You should address the candidate as *du* throughout this role play.

## ■ MARK SCHEME

| | 0 | 1 | 2 | 3 | 4 |
|---|---|---|---|---|---|
| **a)** | | One detail only given | | *Ich habe nach Amerika gefahren. Es war sonnig* | *Ich bin nach Amerika gefahren. Es war sonnig* |
| **b)** | | Wrong tense in **OCR** | | | *Was hast du im Urlaub gemacht?* |
| **c)** | | No reason given in **OCR** | Reason only in **OCR** | Two minor errors in **OCR** | *Mein Lieblingsferienland ist Amerika, denn die Leute sind freundlich* |
| **d)** | Use of *retten* for 'save' | | | | *Ich spare* |

**14**

© John Murray

# ROLE PLAY 8
# CANDIDATE'S ROLE

On the last day of your holiday in Germany you are ill. You ring the doctor to make an urgent appointment.

a) • *Anruf – warum.*
b) • *Zwei Symptome.*
c) • *Termin heute – Grund warum.*
d) • ❗

When you see ❗ you will have to respond to something which you have not prepared.

Your teacher will play the part of the doctor's receptionist and will speak first.

## ■ TO HELP YOU

a) This is fairly obvious – you are ringing because you want to see the doctor. If you don't know the word for 'appointment', then say this instead.
b) Choose two things you can say properly.
c) The rubric at the top tells you what you need to prepare here. Think how you might express 'urgent' if you don't know the actual word.
d) What might a receptionist want to ask over the phone?

## ■ JOT DOWN YOUR ANSWERS

a) _____

_____

b) _____

_____

c) _____

_____

d) _____

_____

# TEACHER'S ROLE

Because the candidate's role is unstructured, it is essential that you are clear about the tasks that the candidate must accomplish. You may change the target language phrases if necessary, e.g. if the candidate's response makes them inappropriate. However, you should remember that if you supply key vocabulary, candidates cannot be rewarded for it.

1. Introduce the situation, then answer the telephone and ask if you can help.
   *Du bist in Deutschland und du rufst eine Klinik an. Ich bin der/die Angestellte.*
   *Klinik Hausmann. Kann ich Ihnen helfen?*

2. Allow the candidate to say that he/she would like to make an appointment.
   Ask the candidate what is wrong. Elicit two details.
   *Was ist los? Beschreiben Sie mir Ihre Symptome.*

3. Allow the candidate to give two details about his/her symptoms.
   Offer the candidate an appointment for next Monday.
   *Wir haben nächsten Montag einen Termin frei.*

4. ❗ Allow the candidate to say why he/she needs the appointment today.
   Say that is OK. Ask the candidate where he/she is now and when he/she can come to the clinic.
   *Das ist O.K. Wo sind Sie im Moment? Um wie viel Uhr können Sie kommen?*

5. Allow the candidate to say where he/she is and when he/she can come to the clinic.
   End the conversation by agreeing.
   *Das geht.*

NB   You should address the candidate as *Sie* throughout this role play.

| OCR | otherwise correct response |
| WO | word order |

## ■ MARK SCHEME

| | 0 | 1 | 2 | 3 | 4 |
|---|---|---|---|---|---|
| **a)** | | Mangled pronunciation of *Termin* in **OCR** Use of *m̲öchte* in **OCR** | | | *Ich möchte den Arzt sehen* |
| **b)** | | One detail only given | | | *Ich habe Kopfschmerzen und Ohrenschmerzen* |
| **c)** | | Use of continuous present in **OCR** | | Two minor errors in **OCR** | *Ich fahre morgen nach England* |
| **d)** | | One detail only given | | | *Ich bin im Hotel. Um zehn Uhr* |

# CANDIDATE'S ROLE

> You have been delayed on your way to your hotel in Germany. You telephone to explain, and you do not want to miss your meal.
>
> **a)** • *Verspätung.*
> **b)** • *Grund dafür.*
> **c)** • *Essen?*
> **d)** • ❗
>
> When you see ❗ you will have to respond to something which you have not prepared.
>
> Your teacher will play the part of the receptionist and will speak first.

## ■ TO HELP YOU

**a)** There are times when the cue word(s) can form part of your answer. Think how to use the word here.
**b)** Choose a reason that fits and that you can say – a car breakdown, perhaps.
**c)** The rubric at the top tells you what you need to prepare here. Remember, a ? means you are expected to ask a question.
**d)** What might the receptionist want to know at this stage?

## ■ JOT DOWN YOUR ANSWERS

**a)** _____

_____

**b)** _____

_____

**c)** _____

_____

**d)** _____

_____

# TEACHER'S ROLE

**1** Introduce the situation, then answer the telephone and ask if you can help.
*Du bist in Deutschland und du rufst ein Hotel an. Ich bin der Empfangschef/die Empfangsdame. Hotel Ritter. Kann ich Ihnen helfen?*

**2** Allow the candidate to say he/she is going to be late.
Ask the candidate what has happened.
*Was ist denn passiert?*

**3** Allow the candidate to explain what has happened.
Say that is a pity.
*Das ist Schade.*

**4** 🔲 Allow the candidate to ask if he/she can have a meal when he/she arrives.
Ask the candidate when he/she expects to arrive. Ask the candidate his/her surname and how to spell it.
*Wann kommen Sie also jetzt an? Wie heißen Sie mit Familiennamen? Wie schreibt man das bitte?*

**5** Allow the candidate to say when he/she expects to arrive, give his/her surname and spell it.
End the conversation by saying you will tell the kitchen staff and there will not be a problem.
*Ich sag in der Küche Bescheid. Es wird kein Problem sein.*

| OCR | otherwise correct response |
|-----|---------------------------|
| WO  | word order                |

NB   You should address the candidate as *Sie* throughout this role play.

## ■ MARK SCHEME

|     | 0 | 1 | 2 | 3 | 4 |
|-----|---|---|---|---|---|
| a)  |   |   | *Ich werde spät sein* |   | *Ich habe Verspätung* |
| b)  |   |   |   |   | Appropriate response, e.g. *Mein Auto hat eine Panne* |
| c)  |   | Use of *wenn* in **OCR** | Incorrect **WO** with modal verb in **OCR** | Two minor errors in **OCR** | *Wann ist das Abendessen?* |
| d)  |   | One detail only given | Two details only given |   | At least three letters pronounced correctly in that part of the response |

© John Murray

# CANDIDATE'S ROLE

> You are talking to your Austrian friend about the new school you are going to in September.
>
> **a)** • *Neue Schule – wo und Wegbeschreibung.*
> **b)** • *Drei Fächer. Warum.*
> **c)** • *Neue Schule – zwei Vorteile.*
> **d)** • ⚠
>
> When you see ⚠ you will have to respond to something which you have not prepared.
>
> Your teacher will play the part of your friend and will speak first.

## ■ TO HELP YOU

**a)** Remember, if there are two parts to an answer you must give both, otherwise you will only get one mark. Don't be put off by *Wegbeschreibung* – you should know that *beschreiben* means describe; think what else the friend wants to know apart from where the new school is.

**b)** Choose three subjects you can say properly. There are several very easy reasons you can give.

**c)** *Vorteile* often occurs as a prompt. Make sure you know it. Finding two things here is not difficult.

**d)** What might your friend ask here? If you have no idea, then remember to listen very carefully to what the teacher says.

## ■ JOT DOWN YOUR ANSWERS

**a)** _____

_____

**b)** _____

_____

**c)** _____

_____

**d)** _____

_____

# TEACHER'S ROLE

1 Introduce the situation, then ask the candidate where the new school is and how he/she will get there.
*Du sprichst mit deinem österreichischen Freund/deiner österreichischen Freundin über deine neue Schule. Ich bin der Freund/die Freundin. Wo ist die neue Schule? Wie kommst du dahin?*

2 Allow the candidate to say where the school is and how he/she will get there.
Ask the candidate which three subjects he/she will study and why.
*Welche Fächer wirst du machen? Warum?*

3 Allow the candidate to say which three subjects he/she will study and why.
Ask the candidate what is good about the new school. Elicit two details.
*Was ist gut an der neuen Schule?*

4 ⚠ Allow the candidate to suggest two advantages about the new school.
Ask the candidate why he/she is not staying at the old school.
*Warum bleibst du nicht an der alten Schule?*

5 Allow the candidate to say why he/she is not staying at the old school.
End the conversation by wishing him/her good luck.
*Alles Gute also.*

NB   You should address the candidate as *du* throughout this role play.

| OCR | otherwise correct response |
|-----|----------------------------|
| WO | word order |

## ■ MARK SCHEME

| | 0 | 1 | 2 | 3 | 4 |
|---|---|---|---|---|---|
| **a)** | | One detail only given | | | *In der Stadtmitte. Ich fahre mit dem Bus* |
| **b)** | | No reason given in **OCR** | Reason only in **OCR** | | Three subjects + appropriate reason |
| **c)** | | One detail only given | | Two minor errors in **OCR** | *Es gibt keine Uniform. Die Schule ist modern* |
| **d)** | | | | | *Die Lehrer sind unfreundlich* |

# CANDIDATE'S ROLE

> You are in Germany. You are returning a faulty pair of trousers you bought recently.
>
> **a)** • *Was – wann gekauft.*
> **b)** • ❗
> **c)** • *Größe, Preis.*
> **d)** • *Lösung.*
>
> When you see ❗ you will have to respond to something which you have not prepared.
>
> Your teacher will play the part of the shop assistant and will speak first.

## ■ TO HELP YOU

**a)** Look carefully at the introduction – it often helps. Here it tells you the tense you will need to use.

**b)** What is the assistant likely to ask here? The obvious things are if you have a receipt or what the exact problem is.

**c)** The size does not have to be a number. You can simply say 'large', etc. Make sure you use the correct currency.

**d)** This is quite a common prompt at this Tier. The obvious solution to suggest is a refund or a replacement.

## ■ JOT DOWN YOUR ANSWERS

**a)** _____

_____

**b)** _____

_____

**c)** _____

_____

**d)** _____

_____

# TEACHER'S ROLE

Because the candidate's role is unstructured, it is essential that you are clear about the tasks that the candidate must accomplish. You may change the target language phrases if necessary, e.g. if the candidate's response makes them inappropriate. However, you should remember that if you supply key vocabulary, candidates cannot be rewarded for it.

1 Begin the conversation by introducing the situation and then greeting the candidate.
*Du bringst etwas zum Geschäft zurück. Ich bin der Verkäufer/die Verkäuferin.*
*Kann ich Ihnen helfen?*

2 ❗ Allow the candidate to say that he/she bought a pair of trousers recently.
Ask the candidate what the problem is.
*Ja. Was ist das Problem?*

3 Allow the candidate to say what the problem is. Ask the candidate what size and how much he/she paid for the trousers.
*Welche Größe war das? Und zu welchem Preis?*

4 Allow the candidate to say what size and how much he/she paid for the trousers.
Tell the candidate that size is no longer in stock.
*Es tut mir Leid, aber wir haben die Größe nicht mehr.*

5 Allow the candidate to propose a solution.
End the conversation by agreeing with the candidate.
*Ja, sicher.*

NB You should address the candidate as *Sie* throughout this role play.

| OCR | otherwise correct response |
|-----|----------------------------|
| WO  | word order |

## ■ MARK SCHEME

|    | 0 | 1 | 2 | 3 | 4 |
|----|---|---|---|---|---|
| a) | Wrong tense | Use of *habe . . . +* infinitive in **OCR** Omission of 'when' | | | *Ich habe diese Hose am Samstag gekauft* |
| b) | | | | | *Es gibt ein Loch* |
| c) | | One detail only given | | 2 minor errors in **OCR** | *Sie ist mittelgroß und hat 40 Euro gekostet* |
| d) | | | Wrong **WO** with modal verb in **OCR** | | *Ich möchte mein Geld zurückhaben, bitte./Haben Sie eine andere Hose in der Größe?* |

# ROLE PLAY 12

# CANDIDATE'S ROLE

> You are in the office of a camp site in Austria as you have lost your watch. It was a present from your parents, so you are keen to find it.
>
> **a)** • *Problem.*
> **b)** • *Beschreibung (zwei Details).*
> **c)** • *Wann (zwei Details). Wo.*
> **d)** • !
>
> When you see ! you will have to respond to something which you have not prepared.
>
> Your teacher will play the part of the site manager and will speak first.

## ■ TO HELP YOU

**a)** Look carefully at the introduction – it's important. Here it tells you about both the vocabulary and the tense you need to use.

**b)** This is a standard lost property task, which should be straightforward.

**c)** Again, both these are standard lost property questions. Prepare something you know you can say.

**d)** Try to think what you would want done next – the obvious thing is for the manager to phone the police.

## ■ JOT DOWN YOUR ANSWERS

**a)** _____

_____

**b)** _____

_____

**c)** _____

_____

**d)** _____

_____

# TEACHER'S ROLE

1   Introduce the situation then ask the candidate if you can help.
    *Wir sind auf einem Campingplatz in Österreich. Ich bin der Manager/die Managerin. Kann ich Ihnen helfen?*

2   Allow the candidate to say that he/she has lost his/her watch.
    Ask the candidate to describe it. Elicit two details.
    *Das tut mir Leid. Können Sie bitte die Armbanduhr beschreiben?*

3   Allow the candidate to give two details about the watch.
    Ask the candidate on what day and when exactly he/she lost the watch and where.
    *An welchem Tag haben Sie die Armbanduhr verloren? Wann genau? Und wo haben Sie die Armbanduhr verloren?*

4   ⚠ Allow the candidate to give two details about when he/she lost the watch and to say where.
    Ask the candidate what he/she wants you to do about the problem.
    *Danke. Was kann ich für Sie machen?*

5   Allow the candidate to say what he/she wants you to do about the problem.
    End the conversation by saying you will do that straightaway.
    *Ich werde das sofort machen.*

| OCR | otherwise correct response |
| WO | word order |

NB   You should address the candidate as *Sie* throughout this role play.

## ■ MARK SCHEME

|  | 0 | 1 | 2 | 3 | 4 |
|---|---|---|---|---|---|
| **a)** | Wrong item lost | *Ich verlieren/verloren meine Uhr* | | | *Ich habe meine Uhr verloren/Ich kann meine Uhr nicht finden* |
| **b)** | | One detail only given | | | Two appropriate details |
| **c)** | | One detail only given | Two details only given | Two minor errors in **OCR** | *Das war gestern um 16 Uhr. Das war in dem Supermarkt* |
| **d)** | | *Können Sie mich anrufen?* | *Können Sie helfen?* | | *Bitte rufen Sie die Polizei an* |

# CANDIDATE'S ROLE

> You and your German friend are arranging to go to the cinema.
>
> **a)** • *Kinos in deiner Gegend (zwei Details).*
> **b)** • !
> **c)** • *Lieblingsfilm und warum.*
> **d)** • *Filme im Fernsehen oder im Kino – deine Meinung (zwei Details).*
>
> When you see ! you will have to respond to something which you have not prepared.
>
> Your teacher will play the part of your friend and will speak first.

## ■ TO HELP YOU

**a)** Remember to give two details, otherwise you will only get one mark.

**b)** Think what you might be asked here – if you are arranging to go out, what is your friend likely to be asking?

**c)** A standard task – make sure you can give a suitable reason.

**d)** Make sure your answer here contains two different details and that they are different from those you have already used.

## ■ JOT DOWN YOUR ANSWERS

**a)** _____

_____

**b)** _____

_____

**c)** _____

_____

**d)** _____

_____

# TEACHER'S ROLE

**1** Introduce the situation and ask about cinemas in the candidate's area. Elicit two details.
*Du sprichst mit deinem deutschen Freund/deiner deutschen Freundin. Ich bin der Freund/die Freundin. Was für Kinos gibt es hier in der Nähe?*

**2** ❗ Allow the candidate to give two details about local cinemas.
Say you will go to the cinema this evening. Ask when and where you will meet.
*Gut. Gehen wir also heute Abend ins Kino. Wo und wann treffen wir uns?*

**3** Allow the candidate to state when and where you will meet.
Ask what his/her favourite film is and why.
*Was ist dein Lieblingsfilm? Warum?*

**4** Allow the candidate to name his/her favourite film and say why he/she likes it.
Ask if he/she prefers to watch films on the television or in the cinema. Elicit two details/reasons.
*Siehst du lieber Filme im Fernsehen oder im Kino? Warum?*

**5** Allow the candidate to give two details/reasons about watching films.
End the conversation by saying you will see him/her later.
*Bis später. Tschüß.*

| OCR | otherwise correct response |
|-----|----------------------------|
| WO  | word order                 |

NB   You should address the candidate as *du* throughout this role play.

## ■ MARK SCHEME

|     | 0 | 1 | 2 | 3 | 4 |
|-----|---|---|---|---|---|
| **a)** | | One detail only given | | | *Es gibt zwei Kinos. Sie sind modern* |
| **b)** | | Omission of one element | | | *Treffen wir uns um sieben Uhr vor dem Kino* |
| **c)** | | Title of film only given | No reason in **OCR** | Two minor errors in **OCR** | *Mein Lieblingsfilm ist . . . Er ist spannend* |
| **d)** | *Im Kino/Fernsehen* with no reason | One detail only given | No concept of 'prefer' in **OCR** | | *Ich mag lieber Filme im Fernsehen. Das Kino ist teuer* |

# ROLE PLAY 14

## CANDIDATE'S ROLE

> You have just been on a camping holiday. You are talking to your German friend about the holiday.
>
> **a)** • *Urlaub.*
> **b)** • *Zwei Gründe warum.*
> **c)** • *Zwei Aktivitäten.*
> **d)** • **!**
>
> When you see **!** you will have to respond to something which you have not prepared.
>
> Your teacher will play the part of your friend and will speak first.

### ■ TO HELP YOU

**a)** Remember to use the past tense – the overall rubric tells you this. It also tells you some of the detail you need to use in your first response, so be exact.
**b)** Think of two reasons why you went camping – these do not have to be complicated.
**c)** A standard task – make sure you can give two activities, and watch the tense.
**d)** Think what you might typically go on to discuss if you have just been talking about your last holiday.

### ■ JOT DOWN YOUR ANSWERS

**a)** _____

_____

**b)** _____

_____

**c)** _____

_____

**d)** _____

_____

# ROLE PLAY 14

# TEACHER'S ROLE

**1** Begin the conversation by asking the candidate how he/she spent his/her last holiday.
*Wie hast du deinen letzten Urlaub verbracht?*

**2** Allow the candidate to say he/she has been on a camping holiday.
Ask the candidate why he/she went camping. Elicit two details.
*Warum bist du zelten gegangen?*

**3** Allow the candidate to give two details about why he/she went camping.
Ask the candidate what he/she did whilst there. Elicit two activities.
*Was hast du da gemacht?*

**4** ❗ Allow the candidate to give two activities he/she did whilst there.
Ask the candidate to tell you something about his/her plans for the winter holidays.
*Sag mir etwas über deine Pläne für die Winterferien.*

**5** Allow the candidate to tell you about his/her plans for the winter holidays.
End the conversation by saying you have no plans for the winter.
*Ich habe noch keine Pläne für den Winter.*

**NB** You should address the candidate as *du* throughout this role play.

| OCR | otherwise correct response |
|-----|----------------------------|
| WO  | word order                 |

## ■ MARK SCHEME

|    | 0 | 1 | 2 | 3 | 4 |
|----|---|---|---|---|---|
| **a)** | Wrong tense | | Ich bin auf einem Campingurlaub gegangen | | Ich bin zelten gegangen |
| **b)** | | One detail only given | | | Es ist billig und entspannend |
| **c)** | | One detail only given. Present tense with two activities | Ich bin Tennis gespielt und Souvenirs gekauft | Two minor errors in **OCR** | Ich habe Tennis gespielt und Souvenirs gekauft |
| **d)** | | | Ski fahren | | Ich fahre nach York |

# ROLE PLAY 15

## CANDIDATE'S ROLE

> You are on a school exchange in Germany. You are asking permission to go to a birthday party with your English friend. You discuss your plans with your German hosts.
>
> **a)**    • *Plan.*
> **b)**    • *Drei Details.*
> **c)**    • **!**
> **d)**    • *Dein letzter Geburtstag.*
>
> When you see **!** you will have to respond to something which you have not prepared.
>
> Your teacher will play the part of your German host and will speak first.

### ■ TO HELP YOU

**a)** Think what you actually need to say here – it is quite straightforward.
**b)** Make sure you give all three details, otherwise you will lose marks.
**c)** Think of the sort of question(s) a host might ask.
**d)** Prepare something you can say, and remember which tense to use – *letzter* is the clue!

### ■ JOT DOWN YOUR ANSWERS

**a)** _____

_____

**b)** _____

_____

**c)** _____

_____

**d)** _____

_____

# TEACHER'S ROLE

1 Begin the conversation by asking the candidate what his/her plans are for the weekend.
*Du sprichst mit dem Vater/der Mutter von deinem deutschen Freund.*
*Ich bin der Vater/die Mutter. Was hast du am Wochenende vor?*

2 Allow the candidate to say he/she wants to go to a birthday party with his/her friend.
Ask the candidate for more details about the party. Elicit three details.
*Kannst du mir noch einige Details über die Party geben?*

3 ❗ Allow the candidate to give three details.
Ask what time and how he/she is coming back.
*Wie kommst du nach Hause? Um wie viel Uhr?*

4 Allow the candidate to say how he/she is coming back and at what time.
Ask the candidate what he/she did for his/her last birthday.
*Und wie hast du deinen letzten Geburtstag gefeiert?*

5 Allow the candidate to describe his/her last birthday.
End the conversation by saying he/she can go.
*Also, du darfst gehen.*

NB   You should address the candidate as *du* throughout this role play.

| | |
|---|---|
| **OCR** | otherwise correct response |
| **WO** | word order |

## ■ MARK SCHEME

| | 0 | 1 | 2 | 3 | 4 |
|---|---|---|---|---|---|
| **a)** | | | Wrong **WO** with modal verb in **OCR** | | *Ich möchte mit meinem Freund zu einer Party gehen* |
| **b)** | | One detail only given | Two details only given | | *Sie ist am Samstag bei Peter. Er hat Geburtstag* |
| **c)** | | One detail only given | | Two minor errors in **OCR** | *Ich fahre mit dem Taxi. Ich komme um 11 Uhr zurück* |
| **d)** | Wrong tense | | | *Ich habe ins Restaurant gegangen* | *Ich bin ins Restaurant gegangen* |

# ROLE PLAY 16
# CANDIDATE'S ROLE

> You are talking to an employment agency in Germany about arranging some holiday work.
>
> **a)** • *Arbeit – was, wo.*
> **b)** • *Arbeitserfahrung.*
> **c)** •
> **d)** • *Arbeitszeit? Geld?*
>
> When you see you will have to respond to something which you have not prepared.
>
> Your teacher will play the part of the agency employee and will speak first.

## ■ TO HELP YOU

**a)** You need to give two straightforward details. Think of a job you can say.
**b)** You may have an actual job, which of course you can use, but if it's something unusual, stick with a job you can say you have done.
**c)** Try to think what else the agency might be interested in finding out.
**d)** Remember that the ? means you have to ask a question, and here there are two separate ones. It is usually better to ask them separately.

## ■ JOT DOWN YOUR ANSWERS

**a)** _____

_____

**b)** _____

_____

**c)** _____

_____

**d)** _____

_____

# TEACHER'S ROLE

**1** Introduce the situation, then greet the candidate and ask if you can help.
*Du besprichst eine Stelle in Deutschland. Ich bin der/die Angestellte. Guten Tag. Kann ich Ihnen helfen?*

**2** Allow the candidate to say what type of work he/she is looking for. Ask the candidate what sort of work he/she has done before.
*Was für Arbeitserfahrung haben Sie?*

**3** ❗ Allow the candidate to say what sort of work he/she has done before.
Ask the candidate why he/she would like to work in Germany.
*Warum möchten Sie in Deutschland arbeiten?*

**4** Allow the candidate to say why he/she would like to work in Germany.
Offer the candidate a job in a hotel. Ask the candidate if he/she has any questions for you.
*Ich glaube, ich habe eine Stelle in einem Hotel. Haben Sie Fragen an mich?*

**5** Allow the candidate to ask about pay and hours of work.
End the conversation by saying what the hours of work are and how much money the candidate will be paid.
*Sie fangen um acht Uhr an und arbeiten bis 16 Uhr. Sie bekommen sieben Euro die Stunde.*

| OCR | otherwise correct response |
|-----|---------------------------|
| WO | word order |

NB You should address the candidate as *Sie* throughout this role play.

## ■ MARK SCHEME

| | 0 | 1 | 2 | 3 | 4 |
|---|---|---|---|---|---|
| **a)** | | | Wrong **WO** with modal verb in **OCR** | | *Ich möchte als Kellner(in) in einem Hotel arbeiten* |
| **b)** | | | | | *Ich habe in einem Supermarkt gearbeitet* Present tense also acceptable |
| **c)** | | | Wrong **WO** with modal verb in **OCR** | Two minor errors in **OCR** | *Ich möchte neue Leute kennen lernen* |
| **d)** | | One detail only given *Wie viel Geld und wie lange? Was ist die Arbeitszeit und was ist das Geld?* | | | *Wie viele Stunden muss ich arbeiten? Wie viel Geld verdiene ich?* |

# ROLE PLAY 17

# CANDIDATE'S ROLE

You and your friends are camping in Austria. Unfortunately, you are having problems with the family in the next tent. You go to reception to complain.

a) • *Problem.*

b) • *Situation mit der Familie (zwei Details).*

c) • *Dein Vorschlag.*

d) • !

When you see ! you will have to respond to something which you have not prepared.

Your teacher will play the part of the site manager and will speak first.

## ■ TO HELP YOU

a) You can use the German word *Problem* in your answer here, but make sure you pronounce it correctly. The same applies to *Familie*.

b) Think of some typical things that might be annoying in this situation and choose two you can say.

c) This is a common prompt – do you know what it means?

d) Try to think what the manager might suggest at this point. If you are unsure, listen even more carefully than usual to your teacher.

## ■ JOT DOWN YOUR ANSWERS

a) _____

_____

b) _____

_____

c) _____

_____

d) _____

_____

# TEACHER'S ROLE

1 Introduce the situation, then ask the candidate if you can help.
   *Wir sind auf einem Campingplatz in Österreich. Kann ich Ihnen helfen?*

2 Allow the candidate to complain about the family.
   Ask the candidate exactly what the family is doing. Elicit two details.
   *Was macht die Familie genau?*

3 Allow the candidate to give two details about the family's behaviour.
   Ask what the candidate wants to do about it.
   *Was wollen Sie also machen?*

4 **!** Allow the candidate to say what he/she wants to do about it.
   Say that is not possible. Suggest to the candidate that he/she speaks to the family.
   *Das geht nicht. Warum sprechen Sie nicht mit der Familie?*

5 Allow the candidate to give a reason for not speaking to the family.
   End the conversation by saying you will speak to the family immediately.
   *Ich werde sofort mit der Familie sprechen.*

NB You should address the candidate as *Sie* throughout this role play.

| OCR | otherwise correct response |
|-----|----------------------------|
| WO  | word order                 |

## ■ MARK SCHEME

|    | 0 | 1 | 2 | 3 | 4 |
|----|---|---|---|---|---|
| a) |   | *Ich habe ein Problem* Use of 'family'/'famille' in **OCR** |   |   | *Ich habe ein Problem mit einer Familie/unseren Nachbarn* |
| b) |   | One detail only given |   |   | *Die Familie ist zu laut und sie trinkt viel* |
| c) |   |   |   | Two minor errors in **OCR** | *Ich möchte einen anderen Platz* |
| d) |   |   |   |   | *Sie sind unfreundlich* |

## CANDIDATE'S ROLE

> You are talking to your Swiss friend about the work experience you have just done.
>
> **a)**   • *Wo.*
> **b)**   • *Dauer. Arbeitsstunden.*
> **c)**   • *Arbeit. Zwei Aktivitäten.*
> **d)**   •
>
> When you see ! you will have to respond to something which you have not prepared.
>
> Your teacher will play the part of your friend and will speak first.

### ■ TO HELP YOU

**a)** Which tense do you need here? You do not necessarily have to talk about your real work experience if that is difficult to say.

**b)** Make sure you give both details, otherwise you will lose a lot of marks.

**c)** Keep your answer simple and make sure you give two activities.

**d)** Try to think what else someone might want to know about your work experience.

### ■ JOT DOWN YOUR ANSWERS

**a)** _____

_____

**b)** _____

_____

**c)** _____

_____

**d)** _____

_____

# TEACHER'S ROLE

**1** Introduce the situation, then ask the candidate where he/she did his/her work experience.
*Ich bin dein Freund/deine Freundin aus der Schweiz. Wo hast du dein Arbeitspraktikum gemacht?*

**2** Allow the candidate to say where he/she did his/her work experience.
Ask the candidate how long it lasted and what the working hours were.
*Wie lange hat es gedauert? Was waren deine Arbeitsstunden?*

**3** Allow the candidate to say how long the work experience lasted and what the working hours were.
Ask the candidate what he/she had to do. Elicit two activities.
*Was hast du bei dem Arbeitspraktikum gemacht?*

**4** 🔲 Allow the candidate to say what he/she did.
Ask the candidate whether he/she would like to work there as a career and why. Elicit two reasons.
*Möchtest du auch später dort arbeiten? Warum (nicht)?*

**5** Allow the candidate to give two reasons why he/she would/would not like to work there.
End the conversation by making an appropriate response.
*Das ist gut/Ich verstehe.*

NB   You should address the candidate as *du* throughout this role play.

| OCR | otherwise correct response |
|-----|----------------------------|
| WO  | word order |

## ■ MARK SCHEME

|     | 0 | 1 | 2 | 3 | 4 |
|-----|---|---|---|---|---|
| **a)** |   | Wrong tense in **OCR** | No verb in **OCR** |   | *Ich habe das in einem Hotel gemacht* |
| **b)** |   | One detail only given |   |   | *Es hat zwei Wochen gedauert. Ich habe sechs Stunden pro Tag gearbeitet* |
| **c)** |   |   |   | Two minor errors in **OCR** | *Ich habe Betten gemacht und geputzt* |
| **d)** |   |   |   |   | *Ja. Das war sehr interessant, und die Leute waren freundlich/Nein. Das war langweilig und schmutzig* |

# CANDIDATE'S ROLE

> You are talking to your Swiss visitor about going out for the day. He/she does not have the same interests as you.
>
> **a)** • *Ausflug – wohin und Transportmittel.*
> **b)** • *Drei Aktivitäten da.*
> **c)** • ❗
> **d)** • *Wie viel Geld. Wann.*
>
> When you see ❗ you will have to respond to something which you have not prepared.
>
> Your teacher will play the part of your visitor and will speak first.

## ■ TO HELP YOU

**a)** Choose a place you can say and be careful with the verb you need for getting there. Make sure it is somewhere you can do the three activities you will be talking about in the next answer.
**b)** Make sure you give three activities, otherwise you will lose marks.
**c)** The overall instructions give you a good idea of what you will have to say here.
**d)** Remember to refer to the correct currency for the country you are in – in this case probably the UK.

## ■ JOT DOWN YOUR ANSWERS

**a)** _____

_____

**b)** _____

_____

**c)** _____

_____

**d)** _____

_____

# TEACHER'S ROLE

1 Introduce the situation, and ask the candidate what you are going to do.
   *Du sprichst mit deinem schweizerischen Freund/deiner schweizerischen Freundin. Ich bin der Freund/die Freundin. Also, was machen wir heute?*

2 Allow the candidate to suggest a place to go and how to get there. Ask what there is to do there. Elicit three activities.
   *Was kann man dort machen?*

3 🔲 Allow the candidate to give three activities.
   Say you do not enjoy any of those and ask what else there is to do.
   *Das alles gefällt mir überhaupt nicht. Gibt es nicht 'was Anderes zu tun?*

4 Allow the candidate to suggest another activity.
   Accept the suggestion. Ask the candidate how much it costs and what time you will go.
   *O.K. Aber was kostet das? Wann fahren wir?*

5 Allow the candidate to say how much it costs and when you are going.
   End the conversation by saying you are looking forward to it.
   *Gut. Ich freue mich darauf.*

NB   You should address the candidate as *du* throughout this role play.

| OCR | otherwise correct response |
|-----|---------------------------|
| WO  | word order |

## ■ MARK SCHEME

|     | 0 | 1 | 2 | 3 | 4 |
|-----|---|---|---|---|---|
| **a)** | | One detail only given / Use of *auf* with transport in **OCR** | | | *Ich möchte nach Felixstowe fahren. Wir fahren mit dem Bus* |
| **b)** | | One detail only given | Two details only given | | *Wir können schwimmen, Tennis spielen und Souvenirs kaufen* |
| **c)** | | | | Two minor errors in **OCR** | *Wir können ins Kino gehen* |
| **d)** | | One detail only given | | | *Das kostet fünf Pfund. Um zwei Uhr* |

© John Murray

# ROLE PLAY 20

# CANDIDATE'S ROLE

Your Austrian exchange partner is staying with you. You suggest going to visit a friend for the evening.

**a)** • *Dein Vorschlag.*

**b)** • *Dein Freund/deine Freundin – Charakter und Beschreibung (drei Details).*

**c)** • *Zwei Aktivitäten.*

**d)** • **!**

When you see **!** you will have to respond to something which you have not prepared.

Your teacher will play the part of your exchange partner and will speak first.

## ■ TO HELP YOU

**a)** Remember, the overall instructions usually help you with at least one part of the role play. *Vorschlag* is a word you need to learn.

**b)** Make sure you give three details, otherwise you will lose a lot of marks.

**c)** Choose two activities you know you can say.

**d)** Try to think what else someone would want to know about the visit.

## ■ JOT DOWN YOUR ANSWERS

**a)** _____

_____

**b)** _____

_____

**c)** _____

_____

**d)** _____

_____

# TEACHER'S ROLE

**1** Introduce the situation, and then ask the candidate what you are going to do this evening.
*Du sprichst mit deinem österreichischen Freund/deiner österreichischen Freundin. Ich bin der Freund/die Freundin. Also, was machen wir heute Abend?*

**2** Allow the candidate to explain that you are going to visit a friend. Ask what sort of person the friend is. Elicit three details.
*Wie ist dein Freund/deine Freundin?*

**3** Allow the candidate to give three details about his/her friend. Ask the candidate what you can do at the friend's house. Elicit two activities.
*Was kann man denn bei deinem Freund/deiner Freundin machen?*

**4** ▮ Allow the candidate to give two activities you can do at the friend's house.
Ask the candidate how you are getting there, how far it is and how long you are staying.
*Wie fahren wir dahin? Wie weit ist es? Wie lange bleiben wir?*

**5** Allow the candidate to say how you are getting there, how far it is and how long you are staying.
End the conversation by agreeing to go.
*O.K. Ich komme mit.*

| OCR | otherwise correct response |
|-----|---------------------------|
| WO  | word order |

NB   You should address the candidate as *du* throughout this role play.

## ■ MARK SCHEME

|     | 0 | 1 | 2 | 3 | 4 |
|-----|---|---|---|---|---|
| **a)** | | | | | *Wir können meine Freundin Ann besuchen* |
| **b)** | | One detail only given | Two details only given | | *Sie ist klein, hat braunes Haar und ist sehr nett* |
| **c)** | | | | Two minor errors in **OCR** | Two 'at home' activities |
| **d)** | | One detail only given | Two details only given | | *Mit dem Bus. Es sind zwei Kilometer. Drei Stunden* |

© John Murray

# CANDIDATE'S ROLE

> Your Austrian friend is staying with you. You are arranging to go out
> for a meal. You do not want to eat something typically British.
>
> a)     • *Deine Meinung.*
> b)     • *Wo. Warum.*
> c)     • *Wann. Wie.*
> d)     • **!**
>
> When you see **!** you will have to respond to something which you
> have not prepared.
>
> Your teacher will play the part of your friend and will speak first.

## ■ TO HELP YOU

a) The overall instructions help you with what you need to say here. *Meinung* is a word you need to learn.
b) Make sure you give both pieces of information, otherwise you will lose marks. These are common question words which occur frequently in role plays.
c) Choose things you know you can say.
d) Try to think what else someone might ask.

## ■ JOT DOWN YOUR ANSWERS

a) _____

_____

b) _____

_____

c) _____

_____

d) _____

_____

# ROLE PLAY 21
# TEACHER'S ROLE

1 Begin the conversation by suggesting the two of you go to a fish and chip café for a meal.
*Dein österreichischer Freund/deine österreichische Freundin wohnt bei dir. Ich bin der Freund/die Freundin. Gehen wir heute Abend zum Fish und Chip Café?*

2 Allow the candidate to disagree and give a reason why.
Ask the candidate where he/she would prefer to eat and why.
*Wo möchtest du lieber essen? Warum?*

3 Allow the candidate to say where he/she would prefer to eat and why.
Ask the candidate when you will go and how you will get there.
*Wann gehen wir? Wie kommen wir dahin?*

4 ⚠ Allow the candidate to say when you will go and how you will get there.
Ask the candidate when he/she would normally go to a restaurant for a meal and why.
*Wann gehst du normalerweise ins Restaurant? Warum?*

5 Allow the candidate to say when he/she would normally go to a restaurant and why.
End the conversation by saying you do too.
*Finde ich auch.*

NB You should address the candidate as *du* throughout this role play.

| | |
|---|---|
| **OCR** | otherwise correct response |
| **WO** | word order |

## ■ MARK SCHEME

| | 0 | 1 | 2 | 3 | 4 |
|---|---|---|---|---|---|
| **a)** | | | | | *Nein, das schmeckt mir nicht* |
| **b)** | | No reason given in **OCR** | Reason only in **OCR** | | *In einem italienischen Restaurant. Ich mag Pizza* |
| **c)** | | | | Two minor errors in **OCR** | *Um sieben Uhr. Wir fahren mit dem Bus* |
| **d)** | | No reason given in **OCR** | Reason only in **OCR** | | *Für meinen Geburtstag, denn es ist teuer* |

42

© John Murray

# ROLE PLAY 22

## CANDIDATE'S ROLE

You had planned to visit your German friend but are not now able to do so. You telephone him/her to explain, and to rearrange the visit.

a) • *Situation.*

b) • *Grund warum.*

c) • *Neuer Termin – warum dann.*

d) • !

When you see ! you will have to respond to something which you have not prepared.

Your teacher will play the part of your friend and will speak first.

### ■ TO HELP YOU

a)  The overall instructions help you with what you need to say here. Think of the simplest way to say it.

b)  Choose something that you can say, but which also makes sense in this context.

c)  Be careful with dates – remember the endings on the numbers.

d)  Try to think what the friend might also want to know before you arrive.

### ■ JOT DOWN YOUR ANSWERS

a) _____

_____

b) _____

_____

c) _____

_____

d) _____

_____

# TEACHER'S ROLE

**1** Introduce the situation then say hello to the candidate and say that you are looking forward to his/her visit.
*Du sprichst mit deinem deutschen Freund/deiner deutschen Freundin. Ich bin der Freund/die Freundin. Hallo . . . (candidate's name). Ich freue mich sehr auf deinen Besuch.*

**2** Allow the candidate to say he/she cannot visit you.
Say it is a shame and ask why not.
*Schade. Warum kommst du nicht?*

**3** Allow the candidate to explain why he/she cannot visit you.
Ask the candidate when he/she can come and why then.
*Wann kannst du also kommen? Warum dann?*

**4** ❗ Allow the candidate to say when he/she can come and why then.
Ask the candidate what you are going to do when he/she visits you.
Elicit two activities.
*Und was machen wir, wenn du kommst?*

**5** Allow the candidate to give two activities which he/she would like to do.
End the conversation by saying that is great.
*Prima.*

NB   You should address the candidate as *du* throughout this role play.

| OCR | otherwise correct response |
|---|---|
| WO | word order |

## ■ MARK SCHEME

|  | 0 | 1 | 2 | 3 | 4 |
|---|---|---|---|---|---|
| **a)** |  |  |  |  | *Ich kann dich nicht besuchen* |
| **b)** |  |  |  |  | *Ich habe mir den Arm gebrochen* |
| **c)** |  | No reason given in **OCR** | Reason only in **OCR** | Two minor errors in **OCR** | *In den Sommerferien. Ich habe mehr Zeit* |
| **d)** |  | One detail only given | *Fußball und Schwimmen* |  | *Ich möchte Fußball spielen und schwimmen* |

# ROLE PLAY 23

## CANDIDATE'S ROLE

> You telephone a hotel in Austria because you have left your expensive wallet there.
>
> **a)** • *Situation.*
> **b)** • **!**
> **c)** • *Daten. Zimmer.*
> **d)** • *Gefunden. Dein Vorschlag.*
>
> When you see **!** you will have to respond to something which you have not prepared.
>
> Your teacher will play the part of the hotel receptionist and will speak first.

### ■ TO HELP YOU

**a)** The overall instructions help you with what you need to say here. Which tense will you need?
**b)** It is not difficult to work out what you are likely to be asked here. Make sure you have several facts ready.
**c)** Be careful with dates – remember the endings on the numbers. *Daten* indicates the plural, so be careful.
**d)** What are you likely to want the hotel to do now?

### ■ JOT DOWN YOUR ANSWERS

**a)** _____

_____

**b)** _____

_____

**c)** _____

_____

**d)** _____

_____

# TEACHER'S ROLE

**1** Introduce the situation, then answer the telephone and ask if you can help.
*Ich bin der Empfangschef/die Empfangsdame im Hotel. Hotel Berghof. Kann ich Ihnen helfen?*

**2** ⚠ Allow the candidate to explain that he/she has left a wallet there. Ask the candidate to describe the wallet exactly. Elicit three details.
*Können Sie die Brieftasche genau beschreiben?*

**3** Allow the candidate to give three details about the wallet. Ask the candidate when he/she stayed at the hotel and in which room.
*Von wann bis wann waren Sie hier? In welchem Zimmer?*

**4** Allow the candidate to say the dates of his/her stay and which room he/she stayed in.
Say the wallet has been found and ask what you should do.
*Wir haben Ihre Brieftasche gefunden. Was soll ich jetzt machen?*

**5** Allow the candidate to say what he/she would like you to do. End the conversation by saying that is fine.
*Das machen wir.*

| OCR | otherwise correct response |
|-----|---------------------------|
| WO  | word order |

NB    You should address the candidate as *Sie* throughout this role play.

## ■ MARK SCHEME

| | 0 | 1 | 2 | 3 | 4 |
|---|---|---|---|---|---|
| **a)** | Use of *verlassen/ abfahren* | | | | *Ich habe meine Brieftasche im Hotel verloren* |
| **b)** | | One detail only given | Two details only given | | *Sie ist klein, braun und aus Leder* |
| **c)** | | One detail only given | | Two minor errors in **OCR** | *Das war vom ersten bis zum vierten Juni. Zimmer elf* |
| **d)** | | | Wrong **WO** with modal verb in **OCR** | | *Können Sie meine Brieftasche nach England schicken?* |

# ROLE PLAY 24

# CANDIDATE'S ROLE

You are talking to your German friend about the next summer holidays. You want to work in Germany for two months.

a) • *Deine Urlaubspläne.*
b) • *Wo und warum.*
c) • *Geld für die Reise.*
d) •

When you see you will have to respond to something which you have not prepared.

Your teacher will play the part of your friend and will speak first.

## ■ TO HELP YOU

a) The overall instructions help you with what you need to say here. Be careful with the word order in your answer.

b) Be sure to give both details. Think of a reason which you can say, but which also fits.

c) You do not have to say a lot to gain full marks here, but prepare it carefully.

d) Listen carefully to what you are asked. Again, your answer need not be complicated.

## ■ JOT DOWN YOUR ANSWERS

a) _____

_____

b) _____

_____

c) _____

_____

d) _____

_____

# TEACHER'S ROLE

**1** Begin the conversation by asking the candidate what he/she is planning for next summer.
*Du sprichst mit deinem deutschen Freund/deiner deutschen Freundin.*
*Was hast du für die nächsten Sommerferien vor?*

**2** Allow the candidate to say he/she wants to work in Germany for two months.
Ask him/her where in Germany he/she wants to work and why.
*Wo in Deutschland möchtest du arbeiten? Warum?*

**3** Allow the candidate to say where he/she wants to work and why.
Ask how he/she will get the money for the journey to Germany.
*Wie wirst du das Geld für die Reise bekommen?*

**4** ! Allow the candidate to say how he/she will get the money for the journey to Germany.
Ask what he/she plans to do after the summer holidays.
*Was machst du nach den Sommerferien?*

**5** Allow the candidate to say what he/she plans to do after the summer holidays.
End the conversation by wishing the candidate good luck with his/her plans.
*Viel Glück mit deinen Plänen.*

| OCR | otherwise correct response |
|-----|----------------------------|
| WO  | word order |

NB   You should address the candidate as *du* throughout this role play.

## ■ MARK SCHEME

| | 0 | 1 | 2 | 3 | 4 |
|---|---|---|---|---|---|
| **a)** | | Two months missing in **OCR** | Wrong **WO** with modal verb in **OCR** | | *Ich möchte für zwei Monate in Deutschland arbeiten* |
| **b)** | | No reason given in **OCR** | Reason only in **OCR** | | *In Berlin, denn es gibt viel zu tun* |
| **c)** | | | | Two minor errors in **OCR** | *Ich spare mein Taschengeld* |
| **d)** | | | | | *Ich werde in die Oberstufe gehen* |

# CANDIDATE'S ROLE

You and your German friend are talking about your best friend.

a) • *Beschreibung deines Freunds/deiner Freundin (drei Details).*
b) • *Sein/ihr Wohnort (zwei Details).*
c) • *Seine/ihre letzten Ferien.*
d) • **!**

When you see **!** you will have to respond to something which you have not prepared.

Your teacher will play the part of your friend and will speak first.

## ■ TO HELP YOU

a) This is straightforward, but watch the adjective endings.
b) Be sure to give both details.
c) Make sure you use the right tense – which one do you need?
d) Listen carefully to what you are asked. What you need to say is not difficult.

## ■ JOT DOWN YOUR ANSWERS

a) _____

_____

b) _____

_____

c) _____

_____

d) _____

_____

# TEACHER'S ROLE

1 Begin the conversation by asking the candidate to describe his/her best friend.
  *Du sprichst mit deinem deutschen Freund/deiner deutschen Freundin.*
  *Wie sieht dein bester Freund/deine beste Freundin aus?*

2 Allow the candidate to describe his/her best friend giving three details.
  Ask where exactly the friend lives. Elicit two details.
  *Wo wohnt er/sie genau?*

3 Allow the candidate to give two details of where the best friend lives.
  Ask what the friend did when he/she was on holiday.
  *Was hat dein Freund/deine Freundin in den letzten Ferien gemacht?*

4 **!** Allow the candidate to say what his/her friend did on holiday.
  Ask the candidate to tell you what he/she and the best friend do together in their free time. Elicit three details.
  *Dein Freund/deine Freundin und du, was macht ihr normalerweise in eurer Freizeit?*

5 Allow the candidate to say what he/she and the best friend do together in their free time.
  End the conversation by saying the candidate and his/her best friend are well suited.
  *Ihr passt gut zusammen.*

| OCR | otherwise correct response |
|-----|----------------------------|
| WO  | word order |

NB    You should address the candidate as *du* throughout this role play.

## ■ MARK SCHEME

|     | 0          | 1                    | 2                          | 3                         | 4                                              |
|-----|------------|----------------------|----------------------------|---------------------------|------------------------------------------------|
| a)  |            | One detail only given| Two details only given     |                           | Er/sie ist klein, hat braune Augen und er/sie ist lustig |
| b)  |            | One detail only given|                            |                           | Er/sie wohnt in der Stadtmitte neben dem Schwimmbad |
| c)  | Wrong tense|                      |                            | Two minor errors in **OCR** | Er/sie hat das Museum besucht                  |
| d)  |            |                      | Fußball, Tennis und Schwimmen |                        | Wir schwimmen, gehen ins Kino und spielen Tennis |

# CANDIDATE'S ROLE

> You have arranged a holiday job in Germany in a restaurant in a hotel. You now want to start later than the agreed date of 8 July. You telephone the hotel manager.
>
> **a)**    • *Problem.*
> **b)**    • *Grund.*
> **c)**    • *Vorschlag.*
> **d)**    • !
>
> When you see ! you will have to respond to something which you have not prepared.
>
> Your teacher will play the part of the hotel manager and will speak first.

## ■ TO HELP YOU

**a)** Remember to simply state the basic problem – you can get the information you need from the overall instructions. Watch the date!

**b)** This is very straightforward as long as you choose something you can say, and which fits.

**c)** Be careful with the word order in your answer.

**d)** Listen carefully to what you are told and asked – try and work out what this might be. The instructions at the top may help again here.

## ■ JOT DOWN YOUR ANSWERS

a) _____

_____

b) _____

_____

c) _____

_____

d) _____

_____

# TEACHER'S ROLE

**1** Introduce the situation, then ask the candidate if you can help.
*Wir sind am Telefon. Ich bin der Hotelmanager/die Hotelmanagerin. Kann ich Ihnen helfen?*

**2** Allow the candidate to say he/she cannot start work on 8 July.
Ask the candidate why he/she cannot start work then.
*Warum können Sie also nicht am achten Juli anfangen?*

**3** Allow the candidate to say why he/she cannot start work on 8 July.
Ask the candidate what he/she wants to do.
*Was wollen Sie also machen?*

**4** ⚠ Allow the candidate to say what he/she wants to do to resolve the problem.
Tell the candidate he/she will not be able to work in the restaurant.
Ask what else the candidate can do.
*Sie können leider nicht im Restaurant arbeiten. Was können Sie noch machen?*

**5** Allow the candidate to say what he/she can do.
End the conversation by saying that is fine.
*Das ist gut.*

NB   You should address the candidate as *Sie* throughout this role play.

| OCR | otherwise correct response |
| WO | word order |

## ■ MARK SCHEME

| | 0 | 1 | 2 | 3 | 4 |
|---|---|---|---|---|---|
| **a)** | Wrong date | | Wrong **WO** with modal verb in **OCR** | | *Ich kann nicht am achten Juli anfangen* |
| **b)** | | | | | *Meine Mutter ist krank* |
| **c)** | | | | Two minor errors in **OCR** | *Ich kann im August arbeiten* |
| **d)** | | | | | Any appropriate hotel job other than working in the restaurant |

## CANDIDATE'S ROLE

> You have bought tickets for you and your friend to see a concert in Germany. Now you cannot go and want to change the tickets.
>
> **a)** • *Problem und warum.*
> **b)** • *Details der Vorstellung.*
> **c)** • *Dein Vorschlag.*
> **d)** • **!**
>
> When you see **!** you will have to respond to something which you have not prepared.
>
> Your teacher will play the part of the ticket seller and will speak first.

### ■ TO HELP YOU

**a)** Remember to simply state the basic problem and give a suitable reason why.

**b)** Do you know what *Vorstellung* means? If not, try and guess and, as always if you are NOT sure what a prompt means, listen very carefully to the teacher.

**c)** Think of the obvious suggestion you might make here.

**d)** Listen carefully – in Higher Tier role plays you must be willing and able to come up with alternatives, especially on the **!** utterance.

### ■ JOT DOWN YOUR ANSWERS

**a)** _____

_____

**b)** _____

_____

**c)** _____

_____

**d)** _____

_____

# TEACHER'S ROLE

1 Begin the conversation by asking the candidate if you can help.
*Wir sind am Telefon. Kann ich Ihnen helfen?*

2 Allow the candidate to say he/she cannot go to the concert and why.
Ask which concert and when.
*Welches Konzert ist das? Und wann?*

3 Allow the candidate to give details of the concert and when it is.
Ask the candidate what he/she wants to do.
*Was wollen Sie machen?*

4 **!** Allow the candidate to say he/she wants to change the tickets.
Say that is not possible, all performances are sold out. Ask what the candidate wants to do now.
*Das ist nicht möglich. Es ist völlig ausverkauft. Was möchten Sie jetzt tun?*

5 Allow the candidate to make another suggestion.
End the conversation by saying that is not a problem.
*O.K. Das ist kein Problem.*

NB  You should address the candidate as *Sie* throughout this role play.

| OCR | otherwise correct response |
|-----|----------------------------|
| WO  | word order                 |

## ■ MARK SCHEME

|    | 0 | 1 | 2 | 3 | 4 |
|----|---|---|---|---|---|
| **a)** | | No reason in **OCR** | Reason only in **OCR** | | *Ich kann nicht zum Konzert gehen. Mein Freund ist krank* |
| **b)** | | One detail only given | | | *Das Rockkonzert am Mittwoch* |
| **c)** | Use of *umsteigen/ umziehen* | | Wrong **WO** with modal in **OCR** | Two minor errors in **OCR** | *Kann ich die Karten umtauschen?* |
| **d)** | | | | | *Kann ich mein Geld zurückhaben?* |

# ROLE PLAY 28

# CANDIDATE'S ROLE

> You have just arrived at your German friend's house. You want to find out what there is to do in the area.
>
> **a)**  • *Aktivitäten?*
> **b)**  • *Deine Freizeitaktivitäten (zwei Details).*
> **c)**  •
> **d)**  • *Dein letzter Kinobesuch (drei Details).*
>
> When you see you will have to respond to something which you have not prepared.
>
> Your teacher will play the part of your friend and will speak first.

## ■ TO HELP YOU

**a)** The ? tells you that you must ask a question. The instructions at the top will also help you.

**b)** Remember to give two details, both of which include a verb, otherwise you will not be able to gain full marks.

**c)** It is sometimes quite difficult to guess what the utterance might be. The key is to listen really carefully to what the teacher says.

**d)** You must give three details – think of three things you might say about a recent cinema visit. Which tense do you need?

## ■ JOT DOWN YOUR ANSWERS

**a)** _____

_____

**b)** _____

_____

**c)** _____

_____

**d)** _____

_____

# ROLE PLAY 28

# TEACHER'S ROLE

**1** Begin the conversation by suggesting you go out.
*Du wohnst bei deinem deutschen Freund/deiner deutschen Freundin.*
*Ich bin der Freund/die Freundin. Wollen wir heute ausgehen?*

**2** Allow the candidate to ask what there is to do.
Say there are all kinds of things to do. Ask the candidate what he/she usually does when he/she goes out. Elicit two details.
*Alles kann man machen. Was machst du normalerweise, wenn du ausgehst?*

**3** ❗ Allow the candidate to give two details of what he/she does when he/she goes out.
Say there is a really good German film at the cinema. Ask what kind of film the candidate likes and why.
*Es gibt einen wirklich guten deutschen Film im Kino. Was für Filme magst du? Warum?*

**4** Allow the candidate to say what kind of film he/she likes and why.
Ask the candidate to tell you about his/her last visit to the cinema. Elicit three details.
*Erzähl mir etwas von deinem letzten Kinobesuch.*

**5** Allow the candidate to give three details about the last film he/she saw.
End the conversation by saying you think the cinema is great.
*Ich finde Kino toll.*

NB   You should address the candidate as *du* throughout this role play.

| OCR | otherwise correct response |
|-----|---------------------------|
| WO  | word order |

## ■ MARK SCHEME

| | 0 | 1 | 2 | 3 | 4 |
|---|---|---|---|---|---|
| **a)** | | | | | *Was kann man hier machen?* |
| **b)** | | One detail only given | *Tennis und Schwimmen* | | *Ich gehe einkaufen und spiele Tennis* |
| **c)** | | No reason in **OCR** | Reason only in **OCR** | Two minor errors in **OCR** | *Krimis. Sie sind spannend* |
| **d)** | | One detail only given | Two details only given | | *Das war letzte Woche. Es war eine Komödie und war sehr gut* |

# ROLE PLAY 29

## CANDIDATE'S ROLE

You are looking for a summer job in Germany where you will be able to use your knowledge of languages. You telephone an employment agency to make enquiries.

a)      • *Job.*

b)      • *Deine Fremdsprachen. Seit wann.*

c)      • *Was für Arbeit. Zwei Möglichkeiten.*

d)      • **!**

When you see **!** you will have to respond to something which you have not prepared.

Your teacher will play the part of the employee and will speak first.

## ■ TO HELP YOU

a) Use the instructions at the top to help you work out your answer.

b) Remember to give two details, otherwise you will not be able to gain full marks. Also, the first part of the prompt is in the plural. How do you use a verb with *seit*?

c) Think of two types of work that you can say.

d) Think what type of question a potential employer might ask here.

## ■ JOT DOWN YOUR ANSWERS

a) _____

_____

b) _____

_____

c) _____

_____

d) _____

_____

# TEACHER'S ROLE

**1** Introduce the situation, then ask the candidate how you can help.
*Du telefonierst mit einem Büro in Deutschland. Ich bin am Telefon. Wie kann ich Ihnen helfen?*

**2** Allow the candidate to say he/she is looking for a summer job in Germany.
Ask the candidate which languages he/she can speak and how long he/she has been learning these languages. Elicit details of two languages.
*Welche Fremdsprachen können Sie sprechen? Seit wann lernen Sie diese Sprachen?*

**3** Allow the candidate to say which languages he/she speaks and how long he/she has been learning them.
Ask what sort of work he/she would like to do. Elicit two possibilities.
*Was für Arbeit möchten Sie denn machen?*

**4** ! Allow the candidate to say what sort of work he/she would like to do.
Say that is quite possible. Ask the candidate whether he/she has already worked in Great Britain. Elicit two details.
*Das ist wohl möglich. Haben Sie schon in Großbritannien gearbeitet? Was haben Sie gemacht?*

**5** Allow the candidate to give two details of his/her work in Great Britain.
End the conversation by saying you think you can find a job for him/her.
*Das ist gut. Ich glaube, wir können eine Stelle für Sie finden.*

| OCR | otherwise correct response |
|-----|---------------------------|
| WO  | word order |

NB   You should address the candidate as *Sie* throughout this role play.

## ■ MARK SCHEME

|     | 0 | 1 | 2 | 3 | 4 |
|-----|---|---|---|---|---|
| **a)** | | Omission of *Sommer/ Deutschland* in **OCR** | | | *Ich möchte im Sommer einen Job in Deutschland* |
| **b)** | | | Omission of one language or time in **OCR** | | *Ich lerne Deutsch und Spanisch seit vier Jahren* |
| **c)** | | | | Two minor errors in **OCR** | *Ich möchte in einem Hotel arbeiten oder in einem Restaurant* |
| **d)** | | One detail only given | | | *Ich habe im Supermarkt gearbeitet. Das war letztes Jahr* |

# ROLE PLAY 30

# CANDIDATE'S ROLE

> You are staying in Germany and your friend has arranged a visit to a castle. You really do not want to go.
>
> **a)** • *Deine Meinung – warum.*
> **b)** • *Dein Vorschlag – warum.*
> **c)** • !
> **d)** • *Lieblingshobby. Wie oft.*
>
> When you see ! you will have to respond to something which you have not prepared.
>
> Your teacher will play the part of your friend and will speak first.

## ■ TO HELP YOU

**a)** Use the instructions at the top to help you work out your answer. Make sure you also give the reason why, otherwise you will lose marks.

**b)** Think of something that you can say, but which also fits.

**c)** It is sometimes more difficult to work out the ! response in this type of role play, so listen carefully if you are not sure what might be asked.

**d)** Make sure you give both details here.

## ■ JOT DOWN YOUR ANSWERS

**a)** _____

_____

**b)** _____

_____

**c)** _____

_____

**d)** _____

_____

**59**

# TEACHER'S ROLE

1 Introduce the situation and say you are looking forward to your visit to the castle.
*Du sprichst mit deinem deutschen Freund/deiner deutschen Freundin. Ich bin der Freund/die Freundin. Heute fahren wir zur Burg. Ich freue mich darauf.*

2 Allow the candidate to disagree and say why.
Ask the candidate what he/she wants to do and why.
*O.K. Was möchtest du denn machen? Warum?*

3 ❗ Allow the candidate to say what he/she wants to do and why. Say you can do that as well. Ask what the candidate does in his/her free time in Great Britain. Elicit two activities.
*O.K. Das können wir auch machen. Was machst du gern in deiner Freizeit in Großbritannien?*

4 Allow the candidate to mention two leisure activities.
Ask what his/her favourite hobby is and how often he/she does it.
*Was ist dein Lieblingshobby? Wie oft machst du das?*

5 Allow the candidate to respond and end the conversation by saying you hope he/she will enjoy the day.
*Hoffentlich gefällt dir der Tag heute.*

| OCR | otherwise correct response |
|-----|---------------------------|
| WO | word order |

NB You should address the candidate as *du* throughout this role play.

## ■ MARK SCHEME

| | 0 | 1 | 2 | 3 | 4 |
|---|---|---|---|---|---|
| a) | | No reason in **OCR** | Reason only in **OCR** | | *Ich möchte die Burg nicht besuchen, denn das ist langweilig* |
| b) | | | | | *Ich möchte schwimmen gehen, denn es ist sonnig* <br> Do not penalise English **WO** after *weil* |
| c) | | One detail only given | *Schwimmen und Tennis* | Two minor errors in **OCR** | *Ich schwimme und spiele Tennis* |
| d) | | One detail only given | | | *Mein Lieblingshobby ist Lesen. Jeden Tag* |

# VOCABULARY

## A

accident   *der Unfall*
airport   *der Flughafen*
to allow   *erlauben*
appointment   *der Termin*
arm   *der Arm*
to arrive   *ankommen*
awful   *furchtbar*

## B

bed   *das Bett*
to begin   *beginnen, anfangen*
better   *besser*
birthday   *der Geburtstag*
to brake   *bremsen*
to break   *brechen*
breakdown   *die Panne*
brown   *braun*
(by) bus   *(mit dem) Bus*
to buy   *kaufen*

## C

to be called   *heißen*
you can   *man kann …*
(by) car   *(mit dem) Auto*
castle   *das Schloss/die Burg*
cathedral   *der Dom*
to change (ticket/goods)   *(um)tauschen*
cheap   *billig*
cinema   *das Kino*
to clean   *putzen*
concert   *das Konzert*
to cost   *kosten*
country   *das Land*
crime film   *der Krimi*

## D

dirty   *schmutzig*
to do   *machen, tun*
doctor   *der Arzt*
to drink   *trinken*

## E

earache   *Ohrenschmerzen*
to earn   *verdienen*
to enjoy   *gefallen*
evening meal   *das Abendessen*
exciting   *spannend*
expensive   *teuer*
eyes   *die Augen*

## F

family   *die Familie*
fast   *schnell*
friend   *der Freund/die Freundin*
friendly   *freundlich*
to be fun   *Spaß machen*

it was fun   *das hat Spaß gemacht*
funny   *lustig*

## G

German   *Deutsch*
Germany   *Deutschland*
to get/receive   *bekommen*
to go camping   *zelten*
to go out   *ausgehen*
great   *toll/prima/wunderbar*

## H

hair   *das Haar*
to have back (money)   *zurückhaben*
headache   *Kopfschmerzen*
history   *Geschichte*
hole   *das Loch*
on holiday   *im Urlaub*
the holidays   *die Ferien*
hour   *die Stunde*
to hurt   *weh tun*

## I

ill   *krank*
to interest   *interessieren*
interesting   *interessant*

## J

job   *der Job*
July   *Juli*

## K

kitchen   *die Küche*

## L

to last   *dauern*
late   *spät*
to be late   *Verspätung haben, spät kommen*
leather (made of)   *(aus) Leder*
leg   *das Bein*
to listen   *hören*
to lose   *verlieren*
a lot/many   *viel(e)*

## M

maths   *Mathe*
to meet   *sich treffen*
to meet (get to know)   *kennen lernen*
modern   *modern*
money   *das Geld*
month   *der Monat*
more   *mehr*
museum   *das Museum*
music   *Musik*

## N

neighbours   *die Nachbarn*

**VOCABULARY**

nice   *nett, schön*
noisy   *laut*

**O**

to be of the opinion/
   think   *meinen*
to organise   *organisieren*

**P**

party   *die Party*
people   *die Leute*
picnic   *das Picknick*
to play   *spielen*
pocket money   *das Taschengeld*
police   *die Polizei*
prefer   *lieber (+ verb)*
problem   *das Problem*
puncture   *die Reifenpanne*

**R**

to recommend   *empfehlen*
refund   *Geld zurückhaben*
relaxing   *entspannend*
restaurant   *das Restaurant*
to ring up   *anrufen*

**S**

to save (money)   *sparen*
school   *die Schule*
to see   *sehen*
to send   *schicken*
sixth form   *die Oberstufe*
size   *die Größe*
to ski   *Ski fahren*
small   *klein*
station   *der Bahnhof*
in summer   *im Sommer*
supermarket   *der Supermarkt*

to swim   *schwimmen*
swimming pool   *das Schwimmbad*

**T**

tall   *groß*
to taste   *schmecken*
telephone number   *die Telefonnummer*
tent   *das Zelt*
there is/are   *es gibt*
there was/were   *es gab*
ticket (plane, etc.)   *die Fahrkarte/das Ticket*
ticket (cinema)   *die Karte*
tomorrow   *morgen*
to   *zu*
town   *die Stadt*
to travel   *fahren*

**U**

unfriendly   *unfreundlich*
uniform   *die Uniform*
urgent   *dringend*
useful   *nützlich*

**V**

to visit   *besichtigen/besuchen*
visit   *der Besuch*

**W**

wallet   *die Brieftasche*
to wash up   *abspülen*
watch   *die Armbanduhr*
to watch television   *fernsehen*
what   *was*
what can you …?   *was kann man …?*
when (question)   *wann/um wie viel Uhr?*
when (conjunction)   *wenn*
to work   *arbeiten*